Back to Basics

ENGLISH

for 9-10 year olds

BOOK ONE

Sheila Lane and Marion Kemp

Alphabetical order

There are 26 letters in the alphabet:
5 vowels and 21 consonants. The vowels are written in their
correct order in this alphabet chart.

Fill in the missing consonants.

a			e			i					o					u				

> When the words in a set begin
> with the **same** letter, look at
> the **second** letter of each word.
>
> e.g. c**a**p c**o**t c**u**t
>
> b**l**ack b**r**ick b**u**n

Write each set of nouns in alphabetical order.

bus _____   city _____   print _____

box _____   crowd _____   portrait _____

bin _____   chair _____   picture _____

> When the words in a set begin
> with the **same two letters**, look
> at the **third letter** of each word.
>
> e.g. ba**b**y ba**l**l ba**t**
>
> gr**a**b gr**i**n gr**o**an

Write each set of verbs in alphabetical order.

burn _____   carry _____   steal _____

buy _____   capture _____   strike _____

build _____   catch _____   stand _____

Make sentences by writing each set of words
in alphabetical order.
Don't forget to put a capital letter and a full stop.

big   a   crocodile   water   _____

into   the   dived   _____

lions   ferocious   the   _____

stalked   zebras   _____

floppy   frogs   five   an   _____

chased   angry   anteater   _____

Using a dictionary

> The words in a dictionary are arranged in **alphabetical order**.
>
> If you are looking for the word e n o r m o u s and you open the dictionary at letter **H**, you must turn the pages **backwards** to the letter **E** for e n o r m o u s.

 Fill in the chart with the word **forwards** or the word **backwards**.

Word wanted	Dictionary opened at...	Turn...
quiet	**P**	forwards
pointed	**O**	
reserve	**Y**	
skeleton	**F**	
towel	**J**	

 Use your dictionary to help you to write the meanings of these mathematical words:

angle _____

diagonal _____

pentagon _____

rectangle _____

square _____

 Use your dictionary to find the words, all beginning with **y**, which mean:

1 a kind of sailing boat _____

2 a substance used in making bread _____

3 the yellow part of an egg _____

4 a kind of food made from milk _____

CHALLENGE

Write the letters in the correct order to make a word meaning:

'a shape with 3 straight sides and 3 angles'.

g l e n r i a t

_____

Comprehension

Read these questions:

1 What colour is a giraffe's tongue?

2 Which animal is born with a tooth on the end of its nose?

3 Which animal wears ear-plugs all day?

Find the answers to the questions in this information.

> Giraffes have long necks and long tongues. A giraffe's black tongue is 45 cms long. It is used to pull leaves from the tops of high trees.
>
> Crocodiles lay eggs. A young crocodile uses its egg tooth to break the shell of its egg. The egg tooth is on the tip of the baby's nose and falls off after hatching.
>
> Bush-babies hunt for their food at night and sleep in the day. When daytime comes, a bush-baby makes its own ear-plugs by curling its ears into two little balls. Then it pushes the plugs into its ear-holes so that daytime noises are shut out.

Write the answers in sentences to the three questions at the top of the page.

1 _____

2 _____

3 _____

Write | true | or | false | at the end of each sentence.

1 A giraffe's tongue is between 4 and 5 cms long. [   ]

2 Young crocodiles hatch from eggs. [   ]

3 Fully grown crocodiles have teeth on the end of their noses. [   ]

4 Bush-babies make ear-plugs from bees' wax. [   ]

Finding key words

A **key** is a device for unlocking a door.

A **key word** is one which is **essential** to the **meaning** of a sentence.

e.g. The snake is a reptile.   T̶h̶e̶ snáke i̶s̶ ̶a̶ reptile.

The 2 important **key words** are <u>snake</u> and <u>reptile</u>.

Tick the 3 important
and cross out the unimportant
words in each sentence.

Write the 3 **key words** here:

1 Shéep g̶i̶v̶e̶ ̶u̶s̶ méat a̶n̶d̶ wóol. **1** <u>sheep</u> **2** <u>meat</u> **3** <u>wool</u>

2 Cows give us milk and meat. **1** _____ **2** _____ **3** _____

3 A fly has six legs. **1** _____ **2** _____ **3** _____

4 Birds have wings and feathers. **1** _____ **2** _____ **3** _____

5 Gorillas and chimpanzees
   are kinds of apes. **1** _____ **2** _____ **3** _____

These sentences have 4
key words.

Write the 4 **key words** here:

6 Bats, birds and butterflies
   all have wings. **1** _____ **2** _____ **3** _____ **4** _____

7 Birds are warm-blooded, but
   reptiles are cold-blooded. **1** _____ **2** _____ **3** _____ **4** _____

8 Swans and ducks have
   webbed feet. **1** _____ **2** _____ **3** _____ **4** _____

9 Pigs give us pork, bacon and
   leather. **1** _____ **2** _____ **3** _____ **4** _____

10 Lions and tigers are fierce
   cats. **1** _____ **2** _____ **3** _____ **4** _____

Write a complete sentence for these 4 **key words**:

tortoises   turtles   _____

hard   shells   _____

Grammar

Common nouns are ordinary naming words, e.g. book

Proper nouns are special names, e.g. Treasure Island

Write the nouns from the box under the correct headings.

		Common nouns	Proper nouns
Jasmin	mountain	_____	_____
car	Canada	woman	_____	_____
river	Alps	Nile	_____	_____
pencil	Easter	_____	_____
		_____	

A collective noun is the name of a group of people or things which are all of one kind. e.g. a swarm of bees

Write a collective noun from the box in each space.

flock   choir   shoal
bunch   crowd   pack

a _____ of singers   a _____ of cards

a _____ of flowers   a _____ of people

a _____ of fish   a _____ of sheep

A compound noun is formed by joining two shorter nouns together. e.g. a teaspoon is a spoon for stirring tea.

Add another noun to each of the following to make compound nouns. Use your dictionary to help you.

tooth _____   door _____   bed _____   egg _____

rain _____   table _____   post _____   moon _____

CHALLENGE

Use your dictionary to help you to make 5 compound nouns each beginning with:

foot {
_____
_____
_____
_____
_____

head {
_____
_____
_____
_____
_____

> Many **verbs** are words of **doing**,
> e.g. run, climb. I <u>climb</u> a tree.
>
> Some **verbs** are words of **being**,
> e.g. am, is, are. I <u>am</u> up in a tree.

 Write each sentence using the correct **verb** from the brackets.

1 The postman (knocked, taught, shone) at the door.

_____

2 The postman (am, is, are) at the door.

_____

3 The children (skated, climbed, sailed) on to the bus.

_____

4 The children (am, is, are) on the bus.

_____

5 I (sleep, swim, fly) in my bed.

_____

6 I (am, is, are) in my bed.

_____

 Write the verbs **am**, **is** or **are** in the spaces.

1 I _____ in the kitchen.

2 My father _____ in the garage.

3 Sam and Sangi _____ in the sitting-room.

4 Who _____ at the door?

5 I _____ the daughter of a nurse.

6 _____ you a member of the scout pack?

7 What _____ those children doing?

8 I _____ up in the tree-house.

9 Grandma _____ on the telephone.

10 They _____ not here today.

Spelling

Singular means **one** of anything.   Plural means **more than one**.

e.g.   one strawberry   e.g.   many strawberries

When a singular noun ends with **-ay -ey -oy -uy**
add **s** to make a plural. e.g. ray ⟶ rays

Write the **plural** of these nouns:

boy _____   day _____   guy _____   tray _____

play _____   toy _____   key _____   journey _____

When a singular noun ends with a consonant, followed by a **y**, change
the **y** to **i**, then add **-es**.   e.g. baby ⟶ babies

Write the **plural** of these nouns:

cherry _____   lady _____   pony _____   fly _____

country _____   story _____   daisy _____   city _____

The nouns in the box change from
letter **f** to letter **v** when they
become plurals.

e.g. li**f**e (singular)
     li**v**es (plural)

wife	life	calf	leaf
shelf	self	wolf	half
loaf	thief	knife	scarf

Write these sentences with the correct spelling.

1 (Wolves, Wolfs) are fierce, wild animals.

_____

2 People who steal are called (thiefs, thieves).

_____

3 (Knifes, Knives) are used for cutting.

_____

4 (Leafs, Leaves) grow on trees.

_____

Punctuation

| An ordinary sentence ends with a **full stop**. | A sentence which asks a question ends with a **question mark**. | A sentence which shows surprise or is a command ends with an **exclamation mark**. |

 Write the correct punctuation at the end of each sentence.

1 What's the matter

2 I like this book

3 Hands up

4 I'm going home

5 Where is it

6 Good gracious

7 How far is it

8 Stop that at once

9 Why are you so slow

10 Which coat is yours

 One use of a **comma** is to separate words which come together in a list.
There is **no** comma when <u>and</u> separates the last two words.
e.g. Go and buy some apples, pears, plums <u>and</u> oranges.

 Punctuate this sentence correctly.

The colours of the rainbow are red   orange   yellow   green
blue   indigo and violet

_____

_____

 Punctuate each sentence using the punctuation marks from the box.

1 [**,** **.**]   I shall need nails   string and a hammer

2 [**?** **,** **,**]   Can I borrow your pen   pencil   rubber and compass

3 [**,** **,** **.**]   He had a pen   a toffee   a pebble and a packet of crisps in his pocket

Looking at words: opposites

When **two** things are entirely **different** from each other,
we call them **opposites**.

Draw lines to show the pairs of words which are **opposites**.

1 heavy	blunt	6 cruel	worse
2 few	shallow	7 rough	kind
3 sharp	light	8 safe	crooked
4 deep	early	9 better	smooth
5 late	many	10 straight	dangerous

Write the meaning of each **pair of opposites**, using your dictionary to help you.

ugly... _unpleasant to look at_

pretty... _____

tame... _____

wild... _____

quiet... _____

noisy... _____

difficult... _____

easy... _____

selfish... _____

generous... _____

Find an **opposite** for each of the adjectives and write it in the puzzle.

expensive

dark

full

modern

nasty

Write the word for 1 - 5 down. It means the **opposite** to dirty.

_____

Prefix and suffix

> A **prefix** is an addition at the **beginning** of a word.
> e.g. kind <u>un</u>kind

Give these words an **opposite** meaning by writing the **prefix un-** in front of each one.

happy _____ truthful _____ easy _____ pleasant _____

safe _____ tidy _____ lucky _____ healthy _____

Write the adjective from the list above which describes:

1 someone who is miserable _____

2 a ladder which is dangerous _____

3 someone who is often ill _____

4 something rather nasty _____

5 a person who tells lies _____

6 a room which is not neat _____

7 someone who is not fortunate _____

8 someone who is anxious _____

> A **suffix** is an addition at the **end** of a word. e.g. air air<u>less</u>

Write the **suffix -less** at the end of each of the following words:

Write the meaning of the word you have made.

home _____ _____

noise _____ _____

hair _____ _____

use _____ _____

sense _____ _____

power _____ _____

CHALLENGE

n n n i i g g e b

Write the letters in the correct order to make a word meaning 'a starting point'. The answer is on this page.

_____

Comprehension

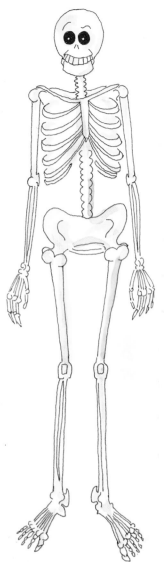

Read these questions:

1 How many bones do you have in your body?

2 Why do you need a skeleton?

3 What is your skin for?

4 How thick is your skin?

Read the information about 'Skin and Bones' to find the answers.

> You have over 200 bones in your skeleton. Without this hard framework you would be like a rag doll and unable to stand up. The main stiffening rod of the skeleton is called the backbone or spine.
>
> The skeleton protects important parts of the body. For example, the ribs make a safe cage for the heart and lungs and the skull protects the brain.
>
> Your skin is only about one millimetre thick. It has many uses. For example, it stops germs from getting into your body; it keeps your temperature steady; it helps to get rid of water by sweating and it has your sense of touch.

Write the answers to the four questions at the top of the page in sentences.

1 _____

2 _____

_____

3 _____

_____

4 _____

Complete this comparison:

A body without a skeleton would be like _____

Write the names of all the bones given in the information.

_____

Making notes

Making notes helps you to remember **important facts**.
By finding **key words** you can write **useful notes**.

 Tick the 3 important **key words** and cross out the unimportant words in each sentence.

1 ~~Your~~ spine ~~is a kind of~~ stiffening rod.

2 The skull protects the brain.

3 The spine is made of bones called vertebrae.

4 The thigh bone is called the femur.

5 The knee bone is called the patella.

 Write the 3 **key words** here:

1 <u>spine</u> 2 <u>stiffening</u> 3 <u>rod</u>

1 _____ 2 _____ 3 _____

1 _____ 2 _____ 3 _____

1 _____ 2 _____ 3 _____

1 _____ 2 _____ 3 _____

Read each sentence.

1 There are twenty-four curved bones in your rib cage.

2 The skull is a kind of bony box which protects your brain.

Write the 5 **key words** here:

1 _____ 2 _____
3 _____ 4 _____ 5 _____

1 _____ 2 _____ 3 _____
4 _____ 5 _____

Read each set of **notes**:

1
| ribs | cage |
| heart | lungs |

2
| skin | one |
| millimetre | thick |

3
| senses | touch | taste |
| smell | sight | hearing |

 Write one complete sentence for each set.

1 _____
_____

2 _____
_____

3 _____
_____

Grammar

Adjectives are words which **describe** nouns.
e.g. an <u>interesting</u> book

Draw a (ring) round the **adjective** in each phrase.

a (misty) morning   the rough sea   a noisy crowd

a wet day   the colourful dress   scrambled eggs

Some **adjectives** are **formed** from **nouns**.

Read these examples:

Noun	Adjective	Example phrase
snow	snowy	a <u>snowy</u> day
beauty	beautiful	a <u>beautiful</u> picture
danger	dangerous	a <u>dangerous</u> rock

Write an **adjective** from each **noun**.

sun __sunny__   truth _____   courage _____

peace _____   fog _____   marvel _____

fame _____   poison _____   rain _____

Write an **adjective** from each **proper noun**.

America __American__   Russia _____   France _____

Germany _____   England _____   Spain _____

Some **adjectives** are formed by adding a **suffix** to a noun.

Read these examples:

Noun	Suffix	Adjective
care	-ful	careful
help	-less	helpless

Add the **suffixes -ful** and **-less** to make **adjectives**.

hope   __hopeful__   cheer _____   _____
      __hopeless__   pain _____

harm _____   rest _____   joy _____

An adjective can be used before or after the noun it describes.
e.g. The grass is <u>green</u>.   How <u>green</u> the grass is!

 Draw a (ring) round the **noun** in each of the following:

 Write the **adjective** which describes the noun.

1 My (house) is painted white.   <u>white</u>

2 I have a woollen sweater.   _____

3 That ladder is dangerous.   _____

4 I like riding in American cars.   _____

5 The choir is very musical.   _____

6 Drive slowly on icy roads.   _____

Adjectives can be used to form **comparisons**.

Read this example:

tall   taller   tallest

Janet is tall.

Eva is taller than Janet.

Patsy is the tallest of the three.

 Complete this chart of **comparisons**:

young	<u>younger</u> youngest		clean	_____	_____
old	older _____		_____	larger	_____
_____	quicker _____		nasty	_____	_____
wise	wiser _____		_____	busier	_____
small	_____ smallest		_____	_____	easiest

 Write a complete sentence in answer to each question:

1 Which is smaller, a bicycle or a bus?
   <u>A bicycle is smaller.</u>

2 Which is bigger, an elephant or an ant?
   _____

3 Which is smallest, a bird, a fly or an aeroplane?
   _____

4 Which is deepest, a puddle, a pond or an ocean?
   _____

English usage

before	after
Use the word **before** to mean, 'earlier than'.	Use the word **after** to mean, 'later than'.

 Complete each sentence with **before** or **after**.

1 In the word 'because' letter a comes _____ letter u.

2 Letter N comes _____ letter M in the alphabet.

3 Don't get off the bus _____ it stops.

4 Put on your socks _____ you put on your shoes.

5 Wash your hands _____ you eat your dinner.

6 The referee stopped the game _____ Sam could shoot a goal.

7 I went inside _____ I had unlocked the door.

8 We left _____ the play ended in order to catch the train.

9 Look _____ you leap!

10 Don't shut the stable door _____ the horse has bolted.

because	although
Use the word **because** for 'giving a reason'.	Use the word **although** to mean 'in spite of'.

Join each pair of sentences with **because** or **although**.

1 Everyone voted for Pat. She was very popular.

   Everyone voted for Pat because she was very popular.

2 Rashid went to school. He was feeling ill.

   _____

3 She felt tired. She had only walked a short distance.

   _____

4 John went to the shop. He wanted to buy a newspaper.

   _____

5 The child ran across the road. It was a dangerous thing to do.

   _____

Looking at words

Draw lines to show the pairs of words which are **synonyms**.

nice	unclean	assist	conceal
nasty	pleasant	ridiculous	courageous
dirty	unpleasant	hide	try
enormous	slim	brave	help
slender	huge	attempt	absurd

Draw a (ring) round the word which is a **synonym** of the word in CAPITAL LETTERS.

VANISH	appear	see	view	disappear
QUANTITY	sip	amount	drink	vast
REGRET	pleasure	retreat	fight	sorrow
WICKED	storm	sinful	good	money
OBSTINATE	stubborn	willing	helpful	daring
EXTERIOR	inside	outside	wall	exit
CIRCULAR	oral	square	round	top
PROHIBIT	break	forbid	support	shatter
PURCHASE	shop	sell	buy	market
FAMOUS	unknown	celebrated	history	people

Draw a (ring) round the **adjective** in each sentence. Rewrite the sentence using **another adjective** having a similar meaning.

1 The child had a (pretty) face. _____

2 It was a pleasant day. _____

3 The ring had a glittering stone. _____

4 I read an exciting book. _____

5 The fat baby gurgled happily. _____

Spelling

Learn to recognize **letter strings**.
e.g. (ight) as in <u>right</u> (tion) as in inven<u>tion</u>.

Draw a ring round the letter strings (ight).

    sight   mighty   delightful
    slight   brightly   frightened

Draw a ring round the letter strings (tion).

    station   education   fractions
    nation   information   protection

Draw rings round these letter strings: (atch) (able) (ough) (edge) .

catches	fable	scratch	rough	stable	snatch
though	gable	hedge	bought	wedge	patch
through	ledge	comfortable	pledge		

Write the words from the box in their four sets.

(atch)	(able)	(ough)	(edge)
_____	_____	_____	_____
_____	_____	_____	_____
_____	_____	_____	_____
_____			

LOOK at each word.   **SAY** each word.   **COVER** each word.   **WRITE** from memory.   **CHECK** your spelling.

vegetables		_____	☐
fraction	$\frac{5}{6}$	_____	☐
light		_____	☐
bough		_____	☐
sledge		_____	☐
matches		_____	☐

Punctuation

Remember –
one use of a **comma** is to separate words which come together in a list.
There is no comma when <u>and</u> separates the last two words.
e.g. I found a pencil, a rubber and two crayons in the bin.

 Write these sentences with correct punctuation.

1 I laid the table with knives forks spoons and plates.

_____

2 The market trader arranged apples pears peaches and bunches of grapes on his stall.

_____

_____

Another use of a comma is to mark a short pause inside a sentence.

e.g. Although it was pouring with rain, I went for a long walk.

 Put **one** comma in each sentence to mark the pause.

1 Although it was nearly time for school Jane lay in bed.

2 In spite of many warnings from their parents the children played in the busy street.

3 If you continue to walk along this path you will eventually reach the main road.

Read these sentences. Put a full stop, a comma, a question mark or an exclamation mark in each balloon.

1 A large ◯ shaggy dog ran out of the farm gate ◯

2 Did you hear me telling you to wear your coat ◯ scarf and gloves ◯

3 After pausing on the edge of the water ◯ the runner took a giant leap over the river ◯

4 How dare you answer me like that ◯

Comprehension

Read these questions.

Write ⌜yes⌝ or ⌜no⌝ or ⌜don't know⌝ after each one.

Is someone who studies the weather called a meteorite? ▭ ▭

Does a thermometer measure temperature? ▭ ▭

Is rainfall measured with a rainbow? ▭ ▭

Does an anemometer measure the speed of wind? ▭ ▭

Read this true information about 'The Weather'.

> Someone who studies the weather is called a meteorologist. A meteorologist measures the temperature of the air with a thermometer. Temperature must be recorded in the shade, out of the direct rays of the sun.
>
> All the air around us has water in it. This is called water vapour. In time, water vapour becomes rain. Rainfall is measured in a rain-gauge.
>
> Wind is moving air. The speed of wind is measured with an instrument called an anemometer. The strength of wind is measured on the Beaufort Scale. A gentle wind is a Force One wind; a hurricane is Force Twelve.

Mark your ⌜yes⌝ and ⌜no⌝ answers with a ⌜✓⌝ or a ⌜✗⌝.
Write ⌜true⌝ or ⌜false⌝ at the end of each sentence.

1 Temperature is recorded in direct sunlight. ▭

2 In time, water vapour becomes rain. ▭

3 A Force One wind is a hurricane. ▭

Complete these sentences with **true** information.

1 Temperature must be recorded in _____.

2 All air contains _____.

3 Wind is caused by _____.

4 The strength of the wind is measured on _____.

Making notes

Read each sentence.

Cross out the words which are **not** important to the meaning.

Write the **key words** from each sentence.

Notes

1 A thermometer tells us how hot or cold the temperature is.

1 _____ 2 _____
3 _____ 4 _____

2 Rainfall is measured with a rain-gauge.

1 _____ 2 _____
3 _____ – _____

3 Wind speed is measured on an anemometer.

1 _____ 2 _____
3 _____ 4 _____

4 The waves on the sea are caused by the wind.

1 _____ 2 _____
3 _____ 4 _____

Read each set of **notes**.

Write a complete sentence for each set.

1 1 hurricane 2 Force
  3 Twelve 4 wind

_____
_____

2 1 trees 2 sway
  3 strong 4 breeze

_____
_____

3 1 thermometer 2 rain-gauge
  3 anemometer 4 instruments
  5 measure 6 weather

_____
_____
_____

4 1 red 2 orange 3 yellow
  4 green 5 blue 6 indigo
  7 violet 8 colours 9 rainbow

_____
_____
_____

CHALLENGE

Make 10 words having 4 or more letters in each, from the word **anemometer**. e.g. moment

_____ _____ _____ _____ _____

_____ _____ _____ _____ _____

Grammar

> A **pronoun** is a word which is used **in place of a noun.**
>
> Read these two sentences:
>
> Barbara cried because <u>Barbara</u> was lost.
>
> Barbara cried because <u>she</u> was lost.
>
> The **pronoun** <u>she</u> is used to avoid using the word Barbara twice in one sentence.

Read the commonly used **pronouns** in the box.

> he   us   him   you   I   they
>
> she   we   her   me   it   them

Draw a (ring) round the **pronouns** in these sentences.

1 Mrs Adams told Robert that he must go to bed.

2 The teacher told us that we must work quietly.

3 We asked Tom's mother if he could come out to play.

4 Mary told Megan that she would give her the book.

5 Will you lend me a pen if I let you borrow my compass?

Rewrite these sentences using **pronouns** instead of the words in red.

1 Jane's aunt took Jane to the cinema.

_____

2 The sun shone and then the sun went behind a cloud.

_____

3 I lent Peter my pen, but Peter lost my pen.

_____

4 Pat and I held up our hands to show that Pat and I were ready.

_____

5 The visitors said goodbye and told Mrs Smith that the visitors would come again.

_____

Parts of speech

A **noun** is a naming word.	An **adjective** describes a noun.	A **pronoun** stands for a noun.	A **verb** tells what is being done.

 Colour in the **one** word in the row which tells you the name of the **part of speech** which the other word belongs to.

ran	walked	verbs	jumped	swam
she	us	it	they	pronouns
brave	adjectives	bold	daring	heroic
house	bungalow	tent	nouns	caravan
adjectives	bright	brilliant	sparkling	luminous

 Use colours to show the different parts of speech in these sentences:

You could use:
red for nouns, green for adjectives, blue for verbs, yellow for pronouns.

1 The warm sun shone in the blue sky.

2 Bright butterflies floated through the tall trees.

3 Ants scuttled round an old jam-pot before they ran away.

4 Busy bees flew among the sweet-scented roses.

5 A bird perched on the low branch until it saw a black cat.

6 The pansies made a yellow carpet as they turned towards the bright sun.

7 Wasps swarmed among the ripe strawberries.

8 The old gardener leant on the gate and smoked his pipe.

CHALLENGE

 Take letters from the end of the first word and from the beginning of the second word to make names of things you can eat.

e.g. portrait artist <u>tart</u>

plastic ornament _____   senior angel _____

shone yellow _____   rumba contest _____

Spelling

Say this spelling rule:

'Letter **i** before **e**, except after **c**,
when it makes the sound **ee**.'

Say the words in both boxes.

i before e
achieve field piece
believe grief yield
chief niece thief

e before i
ceiling deceive receive
conceit deceit receipt
conceited deceived received

 Write the words from the boxes that have the following meanings:

1 to __achieve__ — to do something successfully

2 a _____ — a daughter of your brother or sister

3 to _____ — to accept something which is sent or given

4 to __believe__ — to feel sure that something is true

5 a _____ — a part or bit of something

6 to _____ — to make someone believe something that is not true

> In some words letters **ei** are pronounced like the **ay** in **say**.
> For these words write **e** before **i**.

Say the words in the box.

eight eighty
weight weigh
neigh neigbour
rein vein

 Write the words from the box that have the following meanings:

the number 8   1 __eight__

sound made by a horse   2 _____

a narrow strap for guiding   3 _____

the heaviness of something   4 _____

CHALLENGE

Write the letters in the correct order to make animals' names.

pea _____   shore _____   flow _____

gun _____   bare _____   barged _____

Punctuation

Draw a (ring) round the words which are actually spoken.
Write each sentence with the spoken words in **inverted commas**.

1 (Halt! Who goes there?) shouted the sentry.

"Halt! Who goes there?" shouted the sentry.

2 I am delivering fruit and vegetables, replied the van driver.

_____

3 The soldier on duty said, Let me see your pass.

_____

4 I'm sorry, but I've forgotten it, admitted the driver.

_____

When the speaker's name comes in the **middle** of the words actually spoken, the second part of the sentence begins again with a small letter.   e.g. "I'll give you some money," said her mother, "but don't ask for any more."

Write each sentence with the spoken words in **inverted commas**.

1 Help me across the road, she said, because I'm blind.

_____

2 Tidy up this bedroom, said her mother, or you won't go out to play.

_____

3 Go on, urged the others, and then we'll follow you.

_____

Punctuate each sentence with the punctuation marks from the box.

" "
, ?

Nancy said Why can't I go to the cinema

_____

" "
" "
, , .

Please let me go she continued because all my friends will be there

_____

Comprehension

Read these questions.

Write yes or no or don't know after each one.

1 Is the sun always shining?

2 Are 'cotton wool' clouds a sign of stormy weather?

3 Are hail-stones made of frozen rain drops?

4 Do weather forecasters use crystal balls to predict the weather?

Read this true information about 'Clouds'.

Although the sun is always shining, it may be partly or completely hidden by clouds.

Clouds are masses of small drops of water or ice crystals. Some clouds look like soft, white feathers. Others, which look like cotton wool balls, are a sign of fair weather. Heavy, towering clouds bring rain and storms.

In very warm weather storm clouds can build up and develop into thunder storms. Inside the storm clouds there may be not only rain drops, but also frozen rain drops, called hail-stones. Hail-stones can set off electric charges and so make lightning flashes.

Weather forecasters are helped in their work by receiving pictures from weather satellites.

Mark your yes and no answers with a ✓ or a ✗ .

Write true or false at the end of each sentence.

1 Clouds are masses of snow crystals.

2 Soft, white, feathery clouds bring stormy weather.

3 Clouds are masses of small drops of water or ice crystals.

Answer these questions in sentences:

1 How can hail-stones help to make flashes of lightning?

_____

2 How are weather forecasters helped in their work?

_____

Making notes

 Write the 5 **key words** from each sentence.

Notes

1 Hail-stones are pellets of ice which have been tossed around in a thundercloud.

1 _____ 2 _____
3 _____ 4 _____
5 _____

2 Lightning is a gigantic spark of static electricity.

1 _____ 2 _____
3 _____ 4 _____
5 _____

3 More than a million volts of electricity are needed to make a flash of lightning.

1 _____ 2 _____
3 _____ 4 _____
5 _____

4 The sound of thunder follows the flash of lightning.

1 _____ 2 _____
3 _____ 4 _____
5 _____

Write the **key words** in each sentence as notes.

1 Orion, Perseus and Taurus are the names of constellations of stars.

_____
_____

2 To see a rainbow in the sky, you must stand with your back to the sun and look towards the rain.

_____
_____
_____

Read this paragraph:

if you watch animals and plants closely, you may be able to forecast the weather for yourself. Some flowers close their petals before rain comes. It is said that many birds stop singing before a storm comes.

Write notes for each of the 3 sentences.

1 _____ 2 _____ 3 _____
  _____   _____   _____
  _____   _____   _____

Missing words

Write **one** word from the box which makes sense in the sentence.

1 | pencil   portrait
verse   poem

The artist painted a _____ of my aunt..

2 | friend   girl
people   picture

The woman in the _____ was so like my mother.

3 | storm   noise
scene   fight

I looked at the peaceful _____.

4 | book   bull
city   rain

The angry _____ charged at the gate.

Draw a (ring) round **all** the words which would make sense in the sentence. Choose one to write in the sentence.

1 | ripe   narrow
juicy   sweet

I ate a delicious, _____ apple.

2 | weighty   bulky
heavy   light

The camels were bowed down under their _____ loads.

3 | courageous   broken
heroic   brave

A _____ man jumped into the sea and saved the drowning child.

4 | bright   glittering
dim   brilliant

My eyes were dazzled by the _____ light.

The clue to the missing word in each of these sentences is in the **meaning** of the sentence itself. **Read** all the sentence.

Write the best word you can think of in each space.

1 I saw lions, tigers and many other _____ at the zoo.

2 We _____ a model Elizabethan theatre.

3 They were startled by the _____ noise.

4 Growing in the _____ was a most beautiful rose bush.

5 I burnt my hand on the _____ frying pan.

6 The children _____ round the field at top speed.

7 My family buys _____ at the supermarket every weekend.

8 Our dog _____ after all the stray cats in the area.

What's the word?

The **same** word is missing from each of these speech balloons.

> I wear a _____ on my finger.

> Draw a _____ round the answer.

The **one** word which fits all the sentences is **ring**.

> Did you hear the bell _____?

> Join hands and make a _____.

Skim round the balloons in each set quickly.
Write the **one** missing word which fits each set.

1

> I _____ TV on Sunday evenings.

> When John could tell the time he was given a _____.

> Keep _____ while I get over the wall.

Missing word: _____

2

> Please _____ the fire.

> The parcel was as _____ as a feather.

> This lamp gives a good _____.

Missing word: _____

3

> Will that chair _____ my weight?

> A _____ is a powerful animal.

> I can't _____ the smell of gas.

Missing word: _____

4

> I planted roses in the flower _____.

> When the alarm rang I jumped out of _____.

> The ship sank onto the river _____.

Missing word: _____

CHALLENGE

Write **one** word which means:

1   the foliage of a tree
and sheets of paper in a book.

2   an enclosure for animals
and a writing instrument.

_____

3   the outer covering of a tree trunk
and the sound made by a dog.

4   a musical instrument
and a hollow metal tube connected to a tap.

_____   _____

Test your progress

Write each set of words in **alphabetical order**:

1 unless _____ 2 among _____ 3 drum _____

if _____ against _____ drift _____

so _____ about _____ draw _____

although _____ across _____ dream _____

because _____ after _____ drop _____

Write the **plural** of the following words:

boy _____ berry _____ man _____

life _____ city _____ foot _____

box _____ lady _____ child _____

shelf _____ fly _____ tooth _____

key _____ baby _____ mouse _____

Put the correct **punctuation** in each balloon:

1 Where is your dictionary ◯

2 ◯ What is that strange object ◯◯ asked Tom ◯

3 Kim said ◯◯ I've got an uncle ◯ an aunt
and two cousins ◯

Draw lines to show **opposites**.

masculine	unkind
appear	feminine
kind	disappear
correct	unnecessary
necessary	incorrect

Draw lines to show **synonyms**.

halt	empty
abandon	stop
aid	leave
vacant	help
astonish	surprise

Colour in how many you got right on the ladder and your mistakes on the snake.

50 49 48 47 46 45 44 43 42 41 40 39 38 37 36 35 34 33 32 31 30 29 28 27 26 25 24 23 22 21 20 19 18 17 16 15 14 13 12 11 10 9 8 7 6 5 4 3 2 1

1 2 3 4 5 6 7 8 9 10 11 12 13 14 15 16 17 18 19 20 21 22 23 24 25 26 27 28 29 30 31 32 33 34 35 36 37 38 39 40 41 42 43 44 45 46 47 48 49 50

30

Draw rings round the **common** and **proper nouns**:

1 I have a rubber, a pencil and a ruler in my bag.

2 In the field were cows, sheep, goats and horses.

3 Robert, Ahmet and Marcia are absent today.

4 Have you ever been to Paris, London, Washington or Moscow?

Draw rings round the **verbs**:

1 Fish swim, birds fly and snakes crawl.

2 I jumped out of bed, ran downstairs and opened the door.

3 Who is that?

4 It is the postman.

5 Where are you?

6 I am here.

Draw rings round the **adjectives** in each phrase:

1 a stormy sky

2 an American car

3 a painful cut

4 a beautiful rose

5 the Canadian flag

6 a poisonous berry

7 a slippery fish

8 a miserable face

9 a musical sound

Make an **adjective** from each noun:

1 snow ______________ 2 Russia ______________

3 danger ______________ 4 mist ______________

5 Africa ______________ 6 wonder ______________

Draw rings round the **pronouns**:

1 He had not seen her at the party.

2 John said he would give me a ticket.

3 Will you give it to me please?

4 She said they had found the lost coat.

Colour in how many you got right on the ladder and your mistakes on the snake.

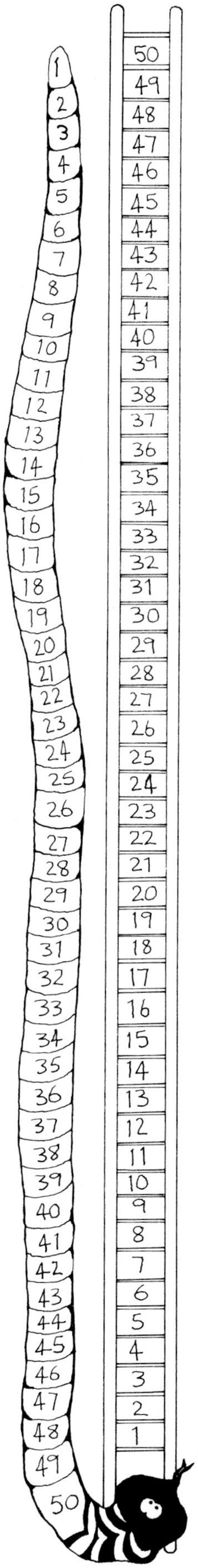
1 2 3 4 5 6 7 8 9 10 11 12 13 14 15 16 17 18 19 20 21 22 23 24 25 26 27 28 29 30 31 32 33 34 35 36 37 38 39 40 41 42 43 44 45 46 47 48 49 50
50 49 48 47 46 45 44 43 42 41 40 39 38 37 36 35 34 33 32 31 30 29 28 27 26 25 24 23 22 21 20 19 18 17 16 15 14 13 12 11 10 9 8 7 6 5 4 3 2 1

Answers

To Parents: We have not provided *all* the answers here. We suggest that items to be drawn on clocks, snakes, etc., should be checked by you. In the case of activities where calculations are performed by your child, it would be good practice to get him/her to use a calculator to check the answers.

Page 2
b,c,d,f,g,h,j,k,l,m,n,p,q,r,s,t,v,w,x,y,z

bin	chair	picture
box	city	portrait
bus	crowd	print
build	capture	stand
burn	carry	steal
buy	catch	strike

A big crocodile dived into the water.
Ferocious lions stalked the zebras.
An angry anteater chased five floppy frogs.

Page 3
forwards backwards forwards forwards
1 yacht 2 yeast 3 yolk 4 yoghurt
triangle

Page 4
1 A giraffe's tongue is black.
2 A crocodile is born with a tooth on the end of its nose.
3 Bush-babies wear ear-plugs all day.
1 False 2 True 3 False 4 False

Page 5
2 1 Cows 2 milk 3 meat
3 1 Fly 2 six 3 legs
4 1 Birds 2 wings 3 feathers
5 1 Gorillas 2 chimpanzees 3 apes
6 1 Bats 2 birds 3 butterflies 4 wings
7 1 Birds 2 warm-blooded 3 reptiles 4 cold-blooded
8 1 Swans 2 ducks 3 webbed 4 feet
9 1 Pigs 2 pork 3 bacon 4 leather
10 1 Lions 2 tigers 3 fierce 4 cats
Tortoises and turtles have hard shells.

Page 6
car	Jasmin
woman	Alps
pencil	Canada
mountain	Nile
river	Easter
choir	pack
bunch	crowd
shoal	flock

e.g. tooth**paste** door**knob/way** bed**post**
egg-**cup**
e.g. rain**bow** table**mat** post**box** moon**beam**
Some answers are:
foot: ball, fall, hill, hold, lights, man, path
head: ache, band, lamp, master, mistress, phone

Page 7
1 knocked 2 is 3 climbed 4 are 5 sleep 6 am
1 am 2 is 3 are 4 is 5 am 6 Are 7 are 8 am
9 is 10 are

Page 8
boys days guys trays
plays toys keys journeys
cherries ladies ponies flies
countries stories daisies cities
1 Wolves 2 thieves 3 Knives 4 Leaves

Page 9
1 ? 2 . 3 ! 4 . 5 ? 6 ! 7 ? 8 ! 9 ? 10 ?
The colours of the rainbow are red, orange, yellow, green, blue, indigo and violet.
1 I shall need nails, string and a hammer.
2 Can I borrow your pen, pencil, rubber and compass?
3 He had a pen, a toffee, a pebble and a packet of crisps in his pocket.

Page 10
2 few, many
3 sharp, blunt
4 deep, shallow
5 late, early
6 cruel, kind
7 rough, smooth
8 safe, dangerous
9 better, worse
10 straight, crooked
1 cheap 2 light 3 empty 4 antique 5 nice clean

Page 11
unhappy untruthful uneasy unpleasant
unsafe untidy unlucky unhealthy
1 unhappy 2 unhealthy 3 unlucky 4 unpleasant
5 untruthful 6 untidy 7 unlikely 8 uneasy
homeless noiseless hairless useless
senseless cheerless powerless
beginning

Page 12
1 You have over 200 bones in your body.
2 You need a skeleton because without the hard framework you would be unable to stand up.
3 Your skin stops germs from getting into your body, keeps your temperature steady, helps to get rid of water by sweating and it has your sense of touch.
4 Your skin is about one millimetre thick.
a rag doll
skeleton backbone spine ribs skull

Page 13
2 1 skull 2 protects 3 brain
3 1 spine 2 bones 3 vertebrae
4 1 thigh 2 bone 3 femur
5 1 knee 2 bone 3 patella
1 1 twenty-four 2 curved 3 bones 4 rib 5 cage
2 1 skull 2 bony 3 box 4 protects 5 brain
1 The ribs make a cage for your heart and lungs.
2 Your skin is one millimetre thick.
3 Your senses are touch, taste, smell, sight and hearing.

Page 14
rough noisy wet colourful scrambled

	truthful
peaceful	foggy
famous	poisonous

	courageous
	marvellous
	rainy

	Russian	French
German	English	Spanish

cheerful, cheerless painful, painless joyful,
harmful, harmless restful, restless joyless

Page 15
2 sweater, woollen 3 ladder, dangerous
4 cars, American 5 choir, musical
6 roads, icy
oldest quick, quickest wisest smaller
cleaner, cleanest large, largest nastier, nastiest
busy, busiest easy, easier
2 An elephant is bigger.
3 A fly is the smallest.
4 An ocean is the deepest.

Page 16
1 before 2 after 3 before 4 before 5 before
6 before 7 after 8 before 9 before 10 after
2 Rashid went to school although he was feeling ill.
3 She felt tired although she had only walked a short distance.
4 John went to the shop because he wanted to buy a newspaper.
5 The child ran across the road although it was a dangerous thing to do.

Page 17
	assist, help
nasty, unpleasant	ridiculous, absurd
dirty, unclean	hide, conceal
enormous, huge	brave, courageous
slender, slim	attempt, try

amount sorrow sinful stubborn outside
round forbid buy celebrated
2 pleasant
3 glittering
4 exciting
5 fat

Page 18
catches	stable	through	hedge
snatch	fable	bought	ledge
scratch	comfortable	though	wedge
patch	gable	rough	pledge

Page 19
1 I laid the table with knives, forks, spoons and plates.
2 The market trader arranged apples, pears, peaches and bunches of grapes on his stall.
1 ... school, Jane ... 2 ... parents, the children ...
3 ... path, you will ...
1, . 2, ? 3, . 4!

Page 20
1 false 2 true 3 false
1 the shade 2 water 3 moving air 4 the Beaufort Scale.

Page 21
1 1 thermometer	2 hot	3 cold	4 temperature
2 1 Rainfall	2 measured	3 rain-gauge	
3 1 Wind	2 speed	3 measured	4 anemometer
4 1 waves	2 sea	3 caused	4 wind

1 A hurricane is a Force Twelve wind.
2 Trees sway in a strong breeze.
3 A thermometer, a rain-gauge and an anemometer are instruments which measure weather.
4 Red, orange, yellow, green, blue, indigo and violet are colours of the rainbow.
Here are some examples. You may have others:
meter name mane meant team meat
eater meteor term tone moan roam

Page 22
1 he 2 us, we 3 We, he 4 she, her
5 you, me, I, you
1 Jane's aunt took her to the cinema.
2 The sun shone and then it went behind a cloud.
3 I lent Peter my pen, but he lost it.
4 Pat and I held up our hands to show that we were ready.
5 The visitors said goodbye and told Mrs Smith that they would come again.

Page 23
verbs pronouns adjectives nouns adjectives

nouns	adjectives
1 sun, sky	warm, blue
2 butterflies, trees	Bright, tall
3 Ants, jam-pot	old
4 bees, roses	Busy, sweet-scented
5 bird, branch, cat	low, black
6 pansies, faces, sun	Yellow, bright
7 Wasps, strawberries	ripe
8 gardener, gate, pipe	old

verbs	pronouns
1 shone	
2 floated	
3 scuttled, ran	they
4 flew	
5 perched, saw	it
6 turned	they
7 swarmed	
8 leant, smoked	it

corn orange honey bacon

Page 24
2 niece 3 receive 4 believe
5 piece 6 deceive
2 neigh 3 rein 4 weight
ape horse wolf
gnu bear badger

Page 25
2 "I am delivering fruit and vegetables," replied the van driver.
3 The soldier on duty said, "Let me see your pass."
4 "I'm sorry, but I've forgotten it," admitted the driver.
1 "Help me across the road," she said, "because I'm blind."
2 "Tidy up this bedroom," said her mother, "or you won't go out to play."
3 "Go on," urged the others, "and then we'll follow you."
Nancy said, "Why can't I go to the cinema?"
"Please let me go," she continued, "because all my friends will be there."

Page 26
1 false 2 false 3 true
1 They can set off electric charges.
2 They receive pictures from weather satellites.

Page 27
1 1 Hail-stones 2 pellets 3 ice 4 tossed
5 thundercloud
2 1 Lightning 2 gigantic 3 spark 4 static
5 electricity
3 1 million 2 volts 3 electricity 4 flash 5 lightning
4 1 sound 2 thunder 3 follows 4 flash 5 lightning
1 1 Orion 2 Perseus 3 Taurus 4 names
5 constellations 6 stars
2 2 rainbow 2 stand 3 back 4 sun 5 look
6 towards 7 rain